BATTLE OF THE
SOMME

ARTHUR McKEOWN

ILLUSTRATED BY
EOIN STEPHENS

POOLBEG
FOR CHILDREN

Published 1999
by Poolbeg Press Ltd
123 Baldoyle Industrial Estate
Dublin 13, Ireland

Text © Arthur McKeown 1999
Illustrations © Eoin Stephens 1999

ISBN 1 85371 931 5

Illustrations by Eoin Stephens
Cover design by Artmark
Set by Poolbeg Group Services Ltd in Times 13.5/20
Printed by ColourBooks Ltd, Baldoyle Industrial Estate,
Baldoyle, Dublin 13, Ireland.

CONTENTS

Chapter 1   THE FARMER GOES TO WAR   1

Chapter 2   LEAVING BALLYMORE   5

Chapter 3   GOING TO ENGLAND   8

Chapter 4   IN FRANCE   13

Chapter 5   GETTING READY FOR BATTLE   19

Chapter 6   THE BATTLE BEGINS   22

Chapter 7   MORE THAN EIGHTY YEARS LATER . . .   30

Chapter 8   AN OLD SOLDIER SPEAKS   34

Arthur Ellis McKeown lives and works in Belfast. He was educated at Roughfort School, at "Inst" in Belfast and the University of Edinburgh. His books for Poolbeg include *Famine, Titanic* and *Robin Hood of the Cave Hill.*

ALSO BY ARTHUR MCKEOWN

Famine
Titanic
Robin Hood of the Cave Hill

PUBLISHED BY POOLBEG

In memory of Samuel Ellis
1888 – 1916

Chapter One

THE FARMER GOES TO WAR

The Great War started at the end of the summer of 1914. In cities, towns and villages all over Europe people were getting ready to fight.

Roy was a farmer. He lived near the village of Ballymore in County Antrim.

He was sitting in the kitchen with his wife Annie. A newspaper lay on the table.

Roy and his wife had three children. Maggie was five years old. Her sister Mary was three. Young John was only two years old. They were all in bed.

"I have to join the army," said Roy quietly. "Everyone has to do what they can."

Annie did not say anything, but Roy could see that she looked worried.

Later that evening Roy went to see his Uncle Willy.

"Everyone must fight if they can, Roy," said Uncle Willy. They were sitting at the kitchen table. "It's our duty. The men have to go to war. The women must do what they can, too. They will do the work on the farms or in the factories."

"What about Annie and the farm?" Roy said.

"Don't worry, Roy, I'll look after Annie and the children while you're away," said Uncle Willy. "I'll look after the farm, too. It won't be a long war. You'll get lots of fresh air and exercise, and you'll get well fed and wear a uniform. You'll get a chance to see the world. Don't worry, Roy, you'll be home for Christmas!"

3

"Yes, Uncle Willy," said Roy. "I'll join the army."

Captain Roberts was a tall man with a brown moustache. Before the war he had been a doctor in Dublin. He had joined the army as soon as the war started.

He was talking to Roy outside the church hall in the middle of Ballymore.

"Well done, Roy," Captain Roberts said. "We need strong young men like you to come to fight."

Lots of other men were there, too. Everyone was asking what they could do to help in the war.

Most of Roy's friends in Ballymore joined the army, too.

Chapter Two
LEAVING BALLYMORE

On the last Sunday in September there was a special service in the church. All the men came with their families. Some people walked. Others came by pony and trap.

The church was full when the service started. The army band played music and everyone sang.

Then the Reverend Moore, an old man with white hair, talked about war and what the men had to do.

"War is a terrible thing!" he said, speaking in a loud, clear voice. "But sometimes men have to fight to protect their families and the country they love. Some of you will die. And how can you die better?

It is a wonderful thing to die in the service of this land we love. Trust in God! He will protect you and look after those you love."

On Monday morning the soldiers got ready to march away.

A photographer came to take pictures of the men in their good clothes. Everyone stood up straight when the light flashed.

Before he left Roy kissed his wife Annie gently. Maggie and Mary stood behind their mother's long skirt.

"Look after the children, Annie," said Roy. "Uncle Willy will help you look after the farm."

Young John was crying. The flash of the camera had frightened him. He did not like all the noise as the men got ready to leave Ballymore for the last time.

"Don't worry, John," said Roy, taking off his cap and tickling the little boy under the chin. "We'll all be home for Christmas."

Maggie and Mary came close to their father and gave him a big hug.

Captain Roberts blew his whistle.

Roy put his cap back on. The men got into lines and started to march away.

The girls stood with their mother as the men went past. Annie was holding young John in her arms. The two girls looked at their mother. She was crying.

Chapter Three
GOING TO ENGLAND

The sun was shining and the sky was blue. It was autumn. The weather was still warm. The leaves on the trees had turned from green to brown. Birds were singing in the trees as the soldiers marched down the hill into Belfast.

The soldiers were tired when they arrived at the big army camp near Belfast. Lots of men from Armagh, Monaghan and Cavan were already there. Men from every part of Ireland were on their way to fight in France.

The next day the soldiers got on board ships for England. Roy stood on the deck of the *Onward* and watched sadly until he could no longer see the coast of Ireland.

The journey across the sea lasted a whole day and night. A few of the soldiers were seasick. Many of them had never been on a ship before.

It was late in the afternoon when Roy and his friends arrived in Liverpool. From there they went to the south of England by train. The soldiers travelled for days. They often had to wait for hours because the railway line was busy. Sometimes the men talked to their friends, or read newspapers, or played cards. The journey was long and boring.

At last they reached Bordon in the south of England.

One day soon after they arrived the soldiers got their uniforms. They all looked smart.

The soldiers had to do a lot of training. They practised fighting. Sometimes they had hard marches in the countryside. Some days they had rifle practice.

Then one day Captain Roberts ordered the soldiers to get into straight lines.

"Men, our training is over!" he said in a loud, clear voice. "We can leave England now. Tomorrow we're going to France!"

All the soldiers cheered and clapped.

At last they were going to war!

Chapter Four

IN FRANCE

Roy and the rest of the men from Ballymore crossed from England to France in October 1915.

The journey from Bordon to the coast took several hours. Roy and his friends watched the English fields and villages as they went past.

The journey was much shorter than the journey from
Liverpool to Bordon, and the sea journey from England to
France was short and quick. It was a warm autumn evening
and the sea was as smooth as glass.

After the soldiers arrived in France they marched many miles to the battlefront. In the distance they could hear the boom of the big guns.

BOOM! BOOM! BOOM!

"What's the name of this place?" one of the soldiers asked.

"It's called the Somme," said Captain Roberts. "That is the River Somme over there, just behind those trees."

"France is just like Ireland," said Billy, one of Roy's friends from Ballymore. "The countryside here looks just the same."

For weeks nothing happened. The winter was long and cold.
Then the spring came. The leaves on the trees turned green.
The birds sang. The sun shone in the blue sky.

The soldiers lived in deep trenches. There was a lot of rain
during the spring. The trenches were full of filthy water.
Mud stuck to the soldiers' uniforms.

Big grey rats lived in the sides of the trenches. They came out at night to look for food which the soldiers had dropped.

It was cold at night in the fields of northern France. Many of the soldiers became sick. Some of them died. The army had very few doctors in France.

Life in the trenches got worse as the months passed.

"The rats seem to be getting bigger!" said Harry, one of the other soldiers from Ballymore. "Will this war never end?"

Chapter Five

GETTING READY FOR BATTLE

Every morning the big German guns boomed for hours.

BOOM! BOOM! BOOM!

The British guns boomed in reply.

BOOM! BOOM! BOOM!

In the evenings Roy and his friends often smoked, or played cards, or talked about their families and friends at home in Ballymore. They remembered the hard work on their farms and the families they had left in Ireland.

Sometimes the men from Ballymore saw other soldiers who had been wounded in the fighting in other places. Some men had bandages on their heads or arms. Some had lost an arm or a leg; and some had bandages on their eyes. Roy and the others heard men crying in pain as they went past on their way to the hospital at the army headquarters.

Then one day Captain Roberts told all the soldiers to get into straight lines.

"Men, we must get ready for battle. Now it's our turn to fight!" he said, speaking loudly and clearly. "I have had our orders from headquarters. There's going to be a great battle soon."

No one cheered or clapped. They had all seen the wounded soldiers who had returned from other parts of the battlefield.

Chapter Six

THE BATTLE BEGINS

The night before the battle some men wrote to their families. Others read their Bibles. No one could sleep.

Dawn broke on the first of July. Birds started to sing in the distance.

The battle started before the sun came up. For hours the guns boomed in the darkness.

BOOM! BOOM! BOOM!

Roy and the other soldiers sat in the trenches. They had their rifles at their sides. They were waiting to go into battle. No one felt like talking.

A big grey rat ran between Roy's feet. He tried to kick it but it got away.

Then, suddenly, the big guns stopped. Everything was quiet.

It was exactly half past seven in the morning. The morning mist was starting to clear away. Captain Roberts stood up and started to climb out of the trench. He had his pistol in his hand. He put his whistle in his mouth and blew it loudly.

"Over the top, men!" he shouted. "Go! Go!"

The men from Ballymore climbed out of the trench, holding their rifles in their hands.

Roy and his friends moved forward in a long, thin line.

The Battle of the Somme had begun.

Captain Roberts died a few minutes later. A bullet hit him in the head. He was dead before his body hit the ground.

The other men from Ballymore were dead by eight o'clock. Shells from the big guns or bullets from machine-guns killed them.

Roy lost both legs when a shell exploded in front of him. He lay screaming in pain for hours before he died. No one was able to help him.

None of the men from Ballymore returned to Ireland. They
all died that morning in the Battle of the Somme.

Chapter Seven

MORE THAN EIGHTY YEARS LATER . . .

Many years later an Irish family went on holiday in France.

Bill was a doctor in Dublin. Jane, his wife, worked for the computer department of a big bank in the city. The family lived near Islandbridge in Dublin. Bill and Jane had two children.

Jack was six. He was going to start school in the autumn. He liked the swimming-pool at the campsite and French food. His sister Patricia was three. She liked playing with the children who were camping in the other tents.

The family spent two weeks at a campsite near Reims. The weather was warm and sunny. They all enjoyed themselves a lot.

It was late June.

Then their holiday was over. Bill packed everything into the back of the family's big BMW.

When everything was nearly ready Bill and Jane had a last cup of coffee. They looked at their map, planning the journey back home.

"Look, Bill, here's the River Somme on the route back to the boat," said Jane, pointing at the map which lay on the table.

"Let's stop there for a while," said Bill. "I'd like to see where my grandfather died. He was killed at the Battle of the Somme. Don't worry, we'll have plenty of time; we should have at least a couple of hours before we have to catch the ferry."

"How much do you know about your grandfather?" asked Jane.

"Not very much," replied Bill. "I just know he was killed on the first morning of the battle. He was only twenty-eight years old. My grandmother had a hard life after he died."

In the back seats of the BMW Jack and Patricia looked out of the windows as the family drove through the French countryside.

"It's just like home," said Jack, watching as they passed the green fields.

Chapter Eight

AN OLD SOLDIER SPEAKS

There were lots of people at the Somme when they arrived.

"I've just realised something," said Jane quietly as they got out of the car. "Today's the first of July. It's the anniversary of the start of the Battle of the Somme. That's why so many people are here."

The family parked their car. They joined the crowds, people of many nationalities, who had come to remember the soldiers who had fought in the battle.

An old Irish officer with lots of medals and a big moustache stood up and came forward on the platform. He began to speak in a loud, clear voice.

"Ladies and gentlemen," he began. "We are here from all parts of Ireland today to remember those who fought in the Battle of the Somme, alongside their brothers from England and other parts of Britain. Many died in the battle. Many more suffered terrible wounds. Many were never seen again.

It was a terrible event in the history of our country. More than 50,000 men from Ireland died or suffered terrible wounds in the weeks and months which followed that terrible first morning. Thousands had to spend the rest of their lives in hospitals.

Families in every part of Ireland lost fathers, sons, brothers, husbands. They were from Ulster and from Connaught; they were from Munster and from Leinster. They came from farms and they came from factories. They came from big cities like Dublin and Belfast; they came from small villages all over the island.

Now let us remember them today."

No one spoke. A skylark flew across the quiet green fields.
After a minute a bugle began to play. People started to move
away in silence. Bill and Jane walked away slowly. Jack and
Patricia walked between their parents, saying nothing.

Soon they were on their way again. They drove in silence.
Jack and Patricia sat quietly in the back of the car. They
watched the flat countryside of northern France slip by.

"We have a boat to catch," said their father after a while,
breaking the long silence. He picked up speed.

They drove on in silence, thinking about everything they had heard from the old soldier and how much the war had meant for so many families in Ireland. Jack and Patricia were soon asleep.

As the sun set slowly in the west Bill drove on quickly.

Robin Hood of the Cave Hill

Naoise O'Haughan was a highwayman. He lived at the back of the Cave Hill in Belfast. He stole money from the rich and gave it to the poor. He was Belfast's Robin Hood!

So begins the story of Belfast's famous outlaw of two hundred years ago, a tale full of excitement and danger. *Robin Hood of the Cave Hill* is delightfully illustrated by Cathy Dineen.

ISBN: 1 85371 264 7

Titanic

The *Titanic* was built in Belfast. Everyone thought she was the best ship in the world. They thought she would never sink. Then one night she hit an iceberg in the middle of the Atlantic . . .

Join Mary as she boards the *Titanic* and begins her voyage on the most luxurious ship of all time. Meet Captain Smith, on his retirement voyage, and Mr Andrews who built the magnificent "unsinkable" ship. Evocatively illustrated by Peter Hogan.

ISBN: 1 85371 516 6

Famine

Joe and his daughter Maggie lived on a farm in Ireland more than one hundred and fifty years ago. In the summer Joe worked in his fields. In the winter he worked at his loom making linen. One morning he went out to the field to check on the potato crop – the potatoes were rotten! All over the country starving families took to the roads. One day Joe was forced to sell the family cow and bought two tickets to America . . . Soon their lives would change forever. Wonderfully illustrated by Josip Lizatovic.

ISBN: 1 85371 505 0

PUBLISHED BY POOLBEG